For Elisabeth and Cecil Collins

Also by Monika Beisner
SECRET SPELLS & CURIOUS CHARMS
MONIKA BEISNER'S BOOK OF RIDDLES
A FOLDING ALPHABET BOOK
AN ADDRESS BOOK

And with Alison Lurie
THE HEAVENLY ZOO
FABULOUS BEASTS

T·O·P·S·Y

The World of Upside Down *The World of Upside Down*

T·U·R·V·Y

With rhymes and pictures by

Monika Beisner

FARRAR STRAUS GIROUX
NEW YORK

To see the Topsy-Turvy World,
Or so I have been told,
You step onto a fleecy cloud
And tightly keep your hold.
Be all eyes, show no surprise,
And wonders will unfold.

What a Topsy-Turvy crazy day,
All that a wooden doll could wish:
The children went up in the sky to play,
The cat was frightened away by a fish,
And into my house a little girl came,
Who sat on my lap and whispered her name.

With paper faces
We meet in high places
Holding our children on strings all the time.
But when the wind blows
As everyone knows
High up in the clouds we allow them to climb.

Our lovely dear old Tom
Was not always terribly nice.
So, for all his lovely breakfasts
He paid a terrible price.
He got up late and found his fate
Was to be a fat meal for mice.

As he strolled by the stream
With his mind on slaughter
The tomcat jumped
When out of the water
A trout popped her head and muttered, "You brute.
Just watch it, you, in your slick gray suit."

White raven, black snow,
Here I sit—poor Joan—
In a cage all alone,
Swinging, swinging, to and fro.

Green roses, red grass,
It is no fun just sitting here,
While the parrot perched so near
Is free to stay or pass.

Yellow sky, blue sun,
At midnight I will hear a scratch,
My friend the mouse will then unlatch
The door and out I'll run.

The stubborn cuckoo was hatching her eggs.
She brooded for years and would not stir.
But poor old cuckoo, what chicks they were!
Not one of them looked in the least like her.
Where are their beaks and feathers and wings?
What are those noses and whiskers and fur?

The sheep had spent a lifetime grazing,
And now they were fed up to the teeth.
The clouds were bored with sailing and gazing
Stupidly down on the fields beneath.
So they changed places, the clouds and the sheep.
I saw it all happen while I was asleep.

The sun sets in the morning,
The waves all race ashore,
The sea gull screams a warning,
The shells begin to roar.

For fear of scalding breezes
I muffle both my hands.
In case the ocean freezes
I skate across the sands.

Come, little girl,
Good little girl,
Let the dog fasten your lead.
We're going for a walk,
A nice long walk.
Exercise is what *you* need.

The dog is pleased with his ice cream,
And, so, the waiter withdraws.
A little girl eyes it wistfully,
The dog slowly rubs his paws.
She puts her hands on the table and begs.
The dog sits back and guffaws.

I'm going to go fishing,
I am, said the Trout,
No messing about,
I'm going to go fishing.

Could do worse,
Ay, said the Pike,
Just as you like,
Could do worse.

What will you catch?
A dish? said the Dace,
Or a pretty face?
What will you catch?

What does it matter?
Said the nervous Eel,
It depends how you feel,
What does it matter?

On the green grassy bank,
Sssh, said the Trout,
Don't all shout,
On the green grassy bank.

With a great splash
Gone was the Trout.
No messing about.
What a great splash.

Jumping Jack
Had a singular knack
Which a great many people adored.
He could capture a girl
And get her to whirl
And twirl on a golden cord.

Jiggety jog, we go up in the sky,
My sweet rocking horse and I,
Gallop a-gallop, then we fly,
Leaving the stars in our wake.
Whoa, whoa, time to go slow.
My back is beginning to ache.

The crowds have scattered and midnight has come,
That's when the circus begins to hum.

The elephant prances around the ring,
The penguins dance and the monkeys sing.

The grizzly bear trundles across the high wire,
The seal juggles tennis balls higher and higher.

And Leo the Lion stands all night
While Isabel gets her act just right:

Like a shimmering butterfly in her attire
She leaps and sails through the hoop of fire.

A hunter who prowled with bow and arrow,
Menacing squirrel and thrush and sparrow,
One night had his weapons stolen away.
Then he heard wings drumming the sky
And saw a great bird and heard it cry,
"Now run for *your* life, you green popinjay."

Rising early late one day,
"Something's up," I said.
Has the gentle sheep got up
On the wrong side of her bed?
She has seated the shepherd boy
And begun to shear his head.

Slowly the full moon rises higher,
You hear the notes of the Three Owls Choir.
    To whit to who.

Beneath the trees is a familiar sight,
The wooden boat heads into the night.
    To whit to who.

In it a little girl may be seen
In a sailor suit of ultramarine.
    To whit to who.

The landlocked sailor sees continents pass
As she steers across the emerald grass.
    To whit to who.

From safe inside the theater box
Our peering eyes grew bolder,
Until we saw a scene to shake
The heart of the beholder,
Punch going thwick with his stick
And Old Nick at his shoulder.

Rockabye, Mommy, in the housetop,
When I am here, your cradle will rock.
I'll sing to you softly, but if you don't sleep,
If you don't sleep,
If you don't sleep,
I'll tumble you out in a horrible heap.

Listen to me, my charming cat!
You, with your pointed claws,
Have frightened all the birds,
From the tits to the jays and jackdaws.
Leave us alone or I'll call in the mice
With their terrible teeth and jaws.

The day winds down to a tidy close.
We each have a place for our nightly repose.
To catch the sweet dreams the darkness unseals
We first do a couple of head-over-heels,
Then the tomcat yawns, curls up on the bed,
And leaves me the floor to rest my head.

Printed in Italy by Federico Motta Editore S.p.A., Milan

Library of Congress catalog card number: 87-045751
ISBN 374-37679-4

Rhymes adapted from the German by Daniel Huws